FRAMEWORKS
38 De Montfort Street, Leicester LE1 7GP, England

First published 1991

British Library Cataloguing in Publication Data
Jones, Merve
  The universe upstairs: a cartoon guide to world views.
  1. Metaphysics
  I. Title II. Sire, James W. *Universe Next Door*
  110

ISBN 0–85111–215–3

Printed and bound in Great Britain
by Cox and Wyman Ltd, Reading

Frameworks is an imprint of Inter-Varsity Press, the book-publishing division of the Universities and Colleges Christian Fellowship.

Contents

Acknowledgments

Any reader experiencing a sense of déjà vu in the contents of this book would not be entirely mistaken. James Sire in *The Universe Next Door* made the very substantial bricks from which this upstairs room is constructed. It was only left to me provide the architecture and the furniture, the friends and, of course, the jam rolls! I am indebted to him for the use of his work and, sometimes, his words in its foundation.

Thank you too Helen, not only for your patient work on this artwork, but for so willingly taking the weight at Spring Graphics while I was trying to concentrate. Thanks to my friends at the church in Downpatrick, who prayed for my continued inspiration. Thanks to any who encouraged – but especially to Pen, my friend and irreplaceable partner in this and everything.

To my parents, Alice and Mervyn,
who gave me more than I realized.

7

OR YOU COULD SAY ~ "OH LORD, OUR LORD, HOW MAJESTIC IS YOUR NAME IN ALL THE EARTH... WHEN I LOOK AT THE HEAVENS, THE WORK OF YOUR HANDS... WHAT IS MAN THAT YOU CARE FOR HIM?" THAT'S PSALM 8.

QUITE A GAP BETWEEN THOSE TWO ~ DIFFERENT WORLDS ~ OR DIFFERENT VIEWS OF THE SAME WORLD.

WELL ~ WE'RE ALL ENTITLED TO OUR OWN OPINION.

MAYBE ~ BUT WHERE'S IT COMING FROM?

"OR WHERE'S IT LEADING TO? WHAT'S YOUR WORLD VIEW? ~ WHY DO YOU THINK THE WAY YOU DO?

ABOUT WHAT?

ABOUT YOURSELF, OTHER PEOPLE, THE WORLD, GOD ~ OR SOME ULTIMATE REALITY.

I JUST MAKE MY DECISIONS AS I GO ALONG.

9

10

IF YOU WANT A DEFINITION "GOD IS INFINITE AND PERSONAL; TRANSCENDENT AND IMMANENT; OMNISCIENT, SOVEREIGN AND GOOD."

HEY! HOLD ON ~ ONE AT A TIME!

O.K.~ GOD IS INFINITE: BEYOND SCOPE OR MEASURE AS FAR AS WE ARE CONCERNED. ALL ELSE IS SECONDARY. HE IS THE ONLY SELF-EXISTENT BEING.

GOD IS ALSO PERSONAL, NOT A FORCE OR ENERGY. HE HAS PERSONALITY ~ THAT IS, HE KNOWS HIM-SELF TO BE, HE THINKS, HE DECIDES AND HE ACTS.

15

TAKE THIS IDEA OF "CHOOSING TO ACT." YOU OFTEN HEAR IT SAID ~ "IT JUST HAPPENED" OR "I COULDN'T HELP IT", AS IF WE SIMPLY REACTED TO CIRCUMSTANCES.

NOT FROM THE THEISTIC POINT OF VIEW ~ I AM FREE TO CHOOSE:

STEP ON MY TOE ~ MUST I CURSE?

ALL IN ALL ~ PERSONALITY IS THE CHIEF THING ABOUT US AS HUMANS ~ AND PROBABLY THE CHIEF THING ABOUT GOD.

FOR INSTANCE, GOD IS ONLY LIMITED BY HIS PERSONALITY: BEING GOOD, HE CANNOT LIE OR ACT WITH EVIL INTENT; BEING MADE BY GOD, OUR PERSONALITY IS BASED ON HIS.

..I MAY. MUST I FORGIVE YOU? I MAY.

MUST I YELL? I MAY.

MUST I SMILE? I MAY.

CLOSE RELATIONSHIP WITH GOD IS "HOME" FOR US.

..SOMEONE TO RELATE TO; A FOCUS FOR KNOWLEDGE; REFUGE FROM ALL FEAR; A RIGHT BASIS FOR JUSTICE; THE SOURCE OF BEAUTY AND CREATIVITY; HIS LOVE IS OUR HOPE OF SALVATION...

WE'RE NOT JUST SMART ANIMALS~ IN CREATING US LIKE HIMSELF, GOD HAS GIVEN US ABILITY AND DIGNITY.

.. WHICH PUTS US SOMEWHERE BETWEEN GOD AND THE REST OF HIS CREATION. BUT..

.. HOW DOES ANYONE KNOW IT'S TRUE? HOW CAN WE KNOW?

BECAUSE GOD HAS MADE US WITH THE CAPACITY TO KNOW HIM AND MAKE SENSE OF THE WORLD AROUND US, AND BECAUSE HE COMMUNICATES WITH US!

GOD TALKS TO PEOPLE?

HE CERTAINLY TAKES THE INITIATIVE.

GOD DOES NOT LOVE US BECAUSE WE'RE VALUABLE; WE ARE VALUABLE BECAUSE GOD LOVES US.

" HE REVEALS HIS THOUGHTS AND HIS CHARACTER TO US IN TWO WAYS ~ GENERAL AND SPECIAL REVELATION.

GENERAL BEING?

" WHAT WE CAN LEARN OF GOD AS WE CONTEMPLATE THE MAGNITUDE AND ORDER OF HIS WORK ~ THE UNIVERSE ··· AND WHEN WE LOOK FROM THAT TO HUMANITY, WE SEE THE DIMENSION OF PERSONALITY ADDED.

NOT VERY SPECIFIC THOUGH.

BUT GOD HAS ALSO MADE HIMSELF KNOWN TO PEOPLE IN MANY SPECIFIC AND SUPER-NATURAL WAYS. THEISTS BELIEVE THAT THE BIBLE IS GOD'S WORD TO HUMANITY···

"In the past God spoke to our forefathers through the prophets . . . but in these last days he has spoken to us by his Son."

HEBREWS 1:1-2

·· THE TEN COMMANDMENTS, THE HEBREW LAWS AND THE PROPHETS. AND FINALLY THERE IS JESUS CHRIST, GOD'S ULTIMATE SPECIAL REVELATION.

20

BECAUSE JESUS CHRIST IS GOD, YET ALSO COMPLETELY HUMAN, HE SHOWS US WHAT GOD IS LIKE MORE FULLY THAN ANY OTHER REVELATION.

SO WE CAN KNOW MUCH OF WHO GOD IS AND WHAT HE WANTS FOR US.

BUT IS THIS THE SAME FOR EVERYONE, EVERY~WHERE, AT ALL TIMES?

YES

··AND YET THERE WAS A MAJOR EVENT IN HISTORY WHICH SEVERELY DAMAGED THAT COMMUNICATION.

IF WE WERE CREATED GOOD~ WE CERTAINLY DIDN'T STAY GOOD.

REMEMBER WE WERE CREATED WITH THE ABILITY TO REASON··

··AND CHOOSE. ADAM AND EVE CHOSE TO DISOBEY THEIR MAKER AT THE ONLY POINT WHERE HE HAD PUT LIMITS.

BUT IF THEY WERE LIMITED ~ THEY WEREN'T FREE!

I'M FREE TO LEAP OFF A TALL BUILDING ~ BUT MY LIMITATIONS WILL SOON BE OBVIOUS WHEN I HIT THE STREET!

The universe is ordered. We were made free *within* the order God created. Our lives are not independent of God even though some may choose to act that way — as Adam and Eve did. The result was death and centuries of personal, social and natural turmoil.

ALL BECAUSE OF ONE DISOBEDIENT ACTION?

17

BECAUSE ALL ASPECTS OF THE IMAGE OF GOD WERE DEFACED.

SOME ARE OBVIOUS: MORALLY ~ WE BECAME LESS ABLE TO TELL GOOD FROM EVIL. SOCIALLY ~ WE BEGAN TO EXPLOIT OTHER PEOPLE. BUT ALSO, WITH OUR INTELLECT NO LONGER LINKED TO ABSOLUTE TRUTH ....

22

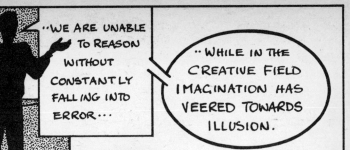

".. WE ARE UNABLE TO REASON WITHOUT CONSTANTLY FALLING INTO ERROR…"

".. WHILE IN THE CREATIVE FIELD IMAGINATION HAS VEERED TOWARDS ILLUSION."

IN PLACE OF OUR ORIGINAL STATUS AS GOD'S CO-GOVERNORS OVER NATURE, WE HAVE BECOME SERVANTS OF NATURE.

THE CONSEQUENCES SEEM OUT OF ALL PROPORTION TO THE SMALLNESS OF THE ACT.

To our minds — fallen remember, it may seem small. If something is already contaminated, a little more pollution is neither here nor there. But from *pure* to *polluted* is a small yet hugely significant step.

BUT THERE'S MORE; BECAUSE GOD IS GOOD, THERE IS HOPE.

THE STORY OF CREATION AND THE FALL TAKES UP THE FIRST THREE CHAPTERS OF THE BIBLE. THE STORY OF GOD'S REDEMPTION PLAN TAKES UP THE REST.

GOD SEARCHES US OUT

··AND "BUYS US BACK", SO TO SPEAK, BY THE PAYMENT OF HIS OWN SON, JESUS CHRIST.

NOT BECAUSE ANY OF US DESERVES IT, BUT BECAUSE GOD WANTS TO GIVE US THE POSSIBILITY OF A NEW LIFE WITH SUBSTANTIAL HEALING, AND TO RESTORE OUR FELLOW-SHIP WITH HIMSELF··YET···

··JUST AS ADAM AND EVE WERE NOT FORCED TO FALL, WE'RE NOT FORCED TO RETURN.

HI, PAUL, WE'RE JUST TAKING IN THE VIEWS OF THE WORLD.

BREATH-TAKING!

SO OVERALL ~ YOU HAVE HUMANITY IN FOUR STAGES:

CREATED: FULLY IN GOD'S IMAGE ~ AND ALL THAT MEANS.

FALLEN: DEFACED, AT ODDS WITH GOD AND HIS CREATION.

REDEEMED: ON THE WAY TO RESTORATION OF THE DEFACED IMAGE OF GOD.

..AND FINALLY GLORIFIED!

HUMANITY TOTALLY HEALED AND AT PEACE WITH GOD, WITH OTHERS AND OURSELVES; SOMETHING THAT ONLY HAPPENS FULLY ON THE OTHER SIDE OF DEATH AND BODILY RESURRECTION.

COMING BACK TO HERE AND NOW~ WE SAY THINGS ARE RIGHT OR WRONG~ HOW CAN WE KNOW?

WE'RE MORAL BEINGS, FLAWED YET STILL REFLECTING SOMETHING OF GOD.

WE LIVE IN A MORAL UNIVERSE AND WHETHER WE HAVE A BASIS FOR OUR MORAL JUDGMENTS, WE FIND OURSELVES MAKING THEM.

IN CHRISTIAN THEISM MORALITY IS NOT RELATIVE BUT MEASURED AGAINST THE ABSOLUTE STANDARD OF GOD HIMSELF .. AND

.. GOD HAS EXPRESSED THIS IN THE BIBLE.

.. THE TEN COMMANDMENTS ~ CHRIST'S SERMON ON THE MOUNT, PAUL'S ETHICAL TEACHING. GOD'S STANDARD IS CLEARLY THERE.

ANYONE WHO WANTS TO KNOW IT, CAN KNOW IT.

28

HOWEVER, IN JESUS WE SEE GOOD LIFE INCARNATE, NOT ONLY PRINCIPLES ~ BUT ACTION

"The Word became flesh and made his dwelling among us ... full of grace and truth."

JOHN 1:14

SO ETHICS IS NOT SOMETHING PEOPLE JUST DREAM UP, OR ADJUST TO SUIT?

NO, GOD IS THE MEASURE OF MORALITY ~ NOT US.

GOD IS CERTAINLY FULLY INVOLVED IN ALL THAT GOES ON ~ IN THE THEIST'S VIEW.

YOU COULD SAY, IN FACT, THAT HISTORY AS A SEQUENCE OF EVENTS IS LEADING TO THE FULFILMENT OF GOD'S PURPOSES FOR HUMANITY.

YOU DON'T THINK IT'S RANDOM THEN?

WELL, WE'RE NOT TALKING ABOUT WHAT I THINK. WE'RE TRYING TO FIND WHAT IS TRUE.

29

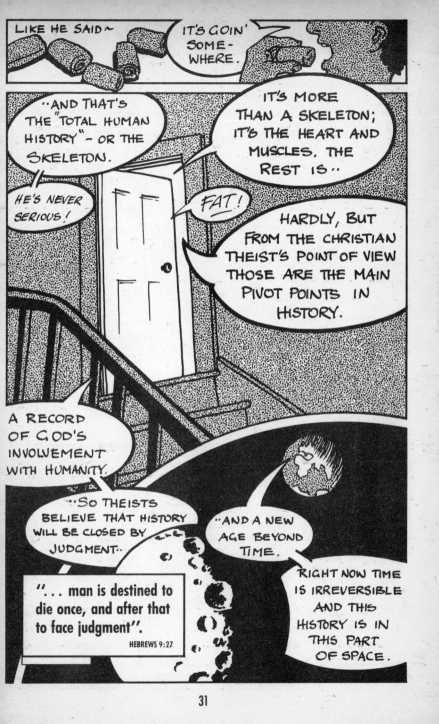

SO, IN CHRISTIAN THEISM YOUR CHOICES HAVE MEANING ~ TO YOU, TO OTHERS, AND TO GOD. HISTORY IS THE RESULT OF THOSE CHOICES.

YET THE MOST IMPORTANT ASPECT IS THAT GOD IS BEHIND IT.

BEHIND APPARENT CHAOS STANDS GOD.

.. BEHIND EVERYTHING, YET IN EVERYTHING.

THE PRIME MOVER, THE UPHOLDER; THE GREATNESS OF GOD IS THE CENTRAL ROCK OF CHRISTIAN THEISM. EVERYTHING FLOWS FROM WHO HE IS.

TO A CHRISTIAN GOD IS MAKER AND SUSTAINER, AND THROUGH JESUS CHRIST, REDEEMER AND FRIEND.

REASON NOW BECAME THE ROUTE TO GOD..

..INSTEAD OF GOD'S SPECIAL REVELATION.

THE INITIATIVE WITH MANKIND, RATHER THAN GOD. WERE DEISTS ANTI-CHRISTIAN?

SOME, LIKE VOLTAIRE, CERTAINLY WERE. OTHERS, LIKE JOHN LOCKE, WERE NOT. HE STILL HELD TO THE IDEA OF GOD'S REVELATION...

..BUT HE INSISTED IT BE JUDGED BY REASON!

SOME BELIEVED IN A PERSONAL GOD, SOME DIDN'T.

DEISM IS MORE A LINK BETWEEN THEISM AND NATURALISM, WHICH FOLLOWED IT, THAN A SCHOOL OF THOUGHT IN ITSELF. BUT THERE ARE SOME BASIC PRINCIPLES.

SO THIS IS WHEN PEOPLE BECAME MACHINES?
NOT YET~ YOU'RE GOING TOO FAST. DEISTS STILL HOLD THAT HUMANS ARE PERSONAL; WE HAVE INTELLIGENCE ~THEY PLACE BIG EMPHASIS ON THAT; A SENSE OF RIGHT AND WRONG; AND A CAPACITY FOR COMMUNITY AND CREATIVITY. BUT IT'S SIMPLY BECAUSE WE'RE MADE THAT WAY.
ALMOST LIKE INSTINCTS.
ALMOST.
~WE ARE WHAT WE ARE, WITH LITTLE HOPE OF EVER BECOMING ANYTHING DIFFERENT ~OR ANYTHING MORE.

WHAT ABOUT THE WORLD AROUND US? OBVIOUSLY IF DEISTS THINK PEOPLE WERE MADE THE WAY THEY ARE...

..THEY THINK THE SAME ABOUT THE UNIVERSE.

THE UNIVERSE IS "NORMAL". DEISTS SEE GOD IN NATURE ~ AS IT IS. HE CAN BE STUDIED, BUT DOESN'T COM-MUNICATE WITH US.

BUT IF ALL KNOWLEDGE COMES FROM STUDYING WHAT IS AROUND US, THAT BRINGS PROBLEMS. WE ARE FINITE AND CANNOT KNOW THE WHOLE. SO IF WE CAN'T, KNOWLEDGE MUST COME FROM ANOTHER SOURCE...

..EITHER BUILT-IN IDEAS OR REVELATION.

HOW DID THE DEISTS RESOLVE THAT?

THEY DIDN'T, AND IT WAS TENSIONS LIKE THAT WHICH MADE DEISM A VERY UNSTABLE WORLD VIEW.

FINDING A REFERENCE POINT FOR ETHICS POSED QUITE A PROBLEM. DEISTS WOULD CLAIM THAT THE UNIVERSE, BEING NORMAL, SHOWS US WHAT IS RIGHT.

THAT IF GOD MADE THE WORLD ~ AND IT'S NOT FALLEN, IT MUST REFLECT WHAT GOD WANTS?

ABSOLUTELY.

..OR AS ALEXANDER POPE SAID IT~

All nature is but art, unknown to thee;
All chance, direction which thou canst not see;
All discord, harmony not understood;
All partial evil, universal good;
And, spite of pride, in erring reason's spite,
One truth is clear; WHATEVER IS, IS RIGHT.

BUT, IF WHATEVER IS, IS RIGHT ~ THEN THERE CAN BE NO EVIL!

..OR, AS BAUDELAIRE SAID ~ JUST TO NAME-DROP A BIT ~ "IF GOD EXISTS, HE MUST BE THE DEVIL."

39

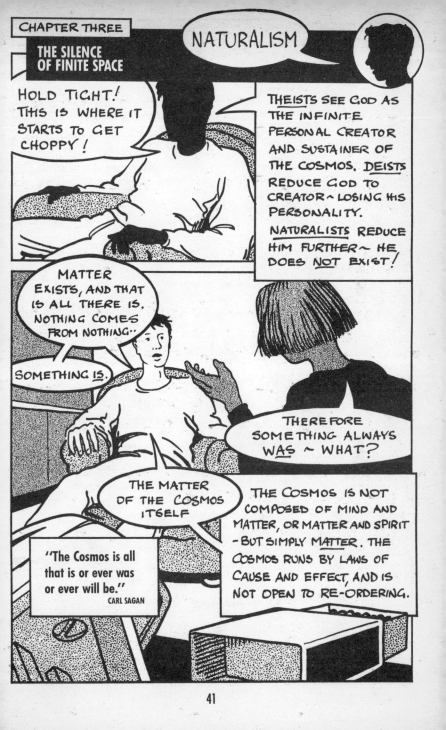

42

.. AND THE LAWS WHICH APPLY TO MATTER APPLY TO US ALSO.

.. AND YET, NATURALISTS INSIST THAT WE ARE DISTINCT FROM THE REST OF THE UNIVERSE AND THAT DISTINCTNESS ~ INTELLIGENCE, CULTURAL SOPHISTICATION AND A SENSE OF RIGHT AND WRONG, ALSO MAKES US VALUABLE.

SOME HOLD THAT HUMAN ACTION IS DETERMINED ~ MORE LIKE RE-ACTION, WHILE OTHERS WOULD LEAVE OPEN THE POSSIBILITY OF SIGNIFICANT HUMAN ACTION...

OUCH!! THAT'S HOT!

"Just another machine ... with the advent of the computer ... This temptation ... becomes more irresistible. 'Can machines think?' now becomes a leading question for our time."

WILLIAM BARRETT

.. OR THE POSSIBILITY OF MORALITY, BECAUSE IF WE'RE NOT FREE TO DO OTHER THAN WE DO, WE CAN'T BE HELD RESPONSIBLE FOR WHAT WE DO! IT'S A BIT WEAK THOUGH.

43

IT IS ~ IT'S OPEN TO CHALLENGE.

.. YOU SEE, BECAUSE ETHICS DID NOT HAVE A CENTRAL ROLE IN THE RISE OF THIS WORLD VIEW ~ NATURALISM CAME MORE FROM IDEAS ABOUT THE <u>EXTERNAL</u> WORLD ~ NATURALISTS TENDED TO BORROW THEIR ETHICAL VIEWS FROM THE SURROUNDING CULTURE.

SO ~ EARLY NATURALIST ETHICS WOULD..

.. HAVE BEEN SIMILAR TO POPULAR CHRISTIAN ETHICS.

~ THE VALUE OF LOVE, TRUTH AND HONESTY, AND RESPECT FOR INDIVIDUAL DIGNITY; WITH JESUS ONLY A TEACHER OF "HIGH" MORAL VALUES.

.. BUT IT'S STILL MUCH THE SAME!

45

ETHICAL VALUES DEPEND ON CONSCIOUSNESS..

..AND FREE WILL.

AND NATURALISTS SAY BOTH CAME WITH THE APPEARANCE OF HUMANS.

MOST NATURALISTS WOULD AGREE WITH THE HUMANIST MANIFESTO II ON THE BASICS FOR ETHICS.

"We affirm that moral values derive their source from human experience. Ethics is *autonomous* and *situational*, needing no theological or ideological sanction. Ethics stems from human need and interest."

HUMANIST MANIFESTO II

..BUT EXACTLY HOW VALUE IS CREATED OUT OF THE HUMAN SITUATION IS COMPLETELY OPEN TO PERSONAL TASTE!

THESE ROPES MUST GO!

IN CHRISTIAN THEISM ETHICS HAVE THEIR SOURCE BEYOND HUMANS IN A GOD WHO IS THE MEASURE OF GOOD, AND HAS REVEALED THAT VALUE TO US.

47

48

IN MUCH THE SAME WAY AS THE INDIVIDUAL ARISES AND DISAPPEARS, HUMANITY, OVER A GREATER TIME SPAN, WILL DO THE SAME.

BANG!!

Natural history began with some self-activating process in the cosmos whereby the universe came into being, and humanity is given its origin in the *theory* of evolution, now taught as fact.

Within the dawn of humanity, this evolution took on a new dimension, for we are free to consider, decide and act. Human actions are *not* simply biological — they are human history.

HOWEVER, EVEN IN SPITE OF OUR SPECIAL NATURE, HUMANITY HAS NO OVERALL PURPOSE.

"Man's intellectual, social and spiritual natures are exceptional among animals in degree, but they arose by organic evolution."

G. C. SIMPSON

HISTORY IS ONLY WHAT WE MAKE IT TO BE; NO MORE. JUST AS WE "APPEARED" - ONE DAY WE WILL DISAPPEAR.

..AND THE UNIVERSE WILL GO ON ALONE.

UPLIFTING STUFF - DO HAVE ANOTHER BERGMAN MOVIE

BUT THAT'S IT REALLY..

YOU CAN GO ON DETOURS..

..SECULAR HUMANISM OR MARXISM, BUT IF YOU'RE AN HONEST NATURALIST, LIFE DOES BECOME A JOLLY BERGMAN ROMP!

TAKE MARX FOR INSTANCE..

..HE WAS INFLUENCED BY HEGEL & FEUERBACH.

HEGEL:

1770-1831

God is an absolute spirit progressively realizing *itself* in the concrete world through conflict with its own opposite. Out of the conflict between spirit and its opposite comes a still higher realization, and so on. For Hegel the highest vehicle as an expression of spirit was human society.

FEUERBACH:

1804-1872

"We are what we eat." Religion is a human invention. God is merely an expression of our unrealized ideals.

Problem: As soon as we invent God we devote ourselves to pleasing our own imaginary construction instead of working to overcome the shortcomings which led to the invention in the first place. He saw Hegel's concept of spirit as a slightly secularized version of Christian God.

MARX:

1818-1883

Marx compounded these two views. Taking Feuerbach's view of religion and yet recognizing that Hegel's idea of absolute spirit and the "still higher by conflict" process could actually be true in human history. Forget the "invented" God — history has proceeded through conflict by contending parties and the goal, says Marx, is a perfect, or ideal, human society (*not* spirit).

SO, ALTHOUGH MARX IS A NATURALIST, HE DOES NOT SEE HISTORY AS HAVING NO PURPOSE.

HE'S MORE INTERESTED IN HISTORY AS PROGRESS..

..THAN IN MATTER ~ THE STATIC PHYSICAL REALITY.

MARX SEES NATURE AS A DYNAMIC PROCESS WITH UNREALIZED POTENTIAL, BEST UNDERSTOOD AS HISTORY.

BECAUSE THERE HE SEES THE CONFLICT THROUGH WHICH THE HIGHER PLANE IS REACHED: THE STRUGGLE TO SURVIVE MORE EFFICIENTLY.

"Man is the supreme being for man ... overthrow all those conditions in which man is an abased, enslaved, abandoned contemptible being."

KARL MARX

PEOPLE ARE MATERIAL, SO...

..MATERIAL AND ECONOMIC FACTORS ARE THE PRIME FORCES IN SHAPING HISTORY.

THE OVERALL VISION IS LIKE THIS:

JAM ROLL TIME AGAIN!

Originally there were small (family-like) tribes — no private property. Each identified with the community as a whole. No technology to assist in the struggle to survive.

As society developed technology the division in labour gradually occurred. Some people controlled the tools and this gave them power to exploit the others. Out of this division and control emerged the *social classes* — the antagonist or negative in Hegel's conflict. (For Marx history is the history of class struggle.) Marx looks at the *system* by which the goods society requires are produced. It's the system that produces the class structure, *e.g.* feudal agriculture or modern industrial capitalism produces a particular class structure. In turn, on that class structure depends what Marx calls the superstructure: art, religion, philosophy, morality, and politics.

Social changes occur with changes in the system of production. The new economic system produces an emerging class which becomes powerful and sweeps away the old dominant class and superstructure and a new order reflecting the new economic order is installed.

In the French Revolution Marx saw an example of this with the triumph of the new middle class, controllers of production. So the forces that create capitalism will also destroy it. Each over-thrower in turn becomes the oppressor.

52

Capitalism requires a large body of propertyless workers to exploit.

Marx reckoned, however, on a build up of more and more workers, with wealth concentrated in the hands of fewer and fewer, so more is produced than can be sold, leading to unemployment and suffering and finally revolution.

The revolt of the workers, however, will be different from any in the past.

They are now in the majority with technology to create an abundance without oppression. And a new classless society will emerge. From the struggle a new and higher form of human life will emerge, working for the good of all.

MARX CLAIMED THAT HIS SOCIALISM WAS ROOTED IN HISTORICAL FORCES, AND NOT A MERE UTOPIAN DREAM.

HE WAS SENSITIVE TO POVERTY AND THE LOSS OF DIGNITY WHEN PEOPLE WERE TREATED LIKE COGS IN A MACHINE..

..HE LOOKED FORWARD TO A CREATIVE APPROACH TO WORK.

BUT WHAT BASIS HAD MARX FOR BELIEVING THAT WE'RE HEADING FOR AN IDEAL SOCIETY?

PURELY HIS PREDICTION BASED ON HIS ANALYSIS OF HISTORY AND ECONOMIC FORCES.

THE PROBLEM LAY IN HIS VIEW OF HUMAN NATURE...

..AND HIS BELIEF THAT GREED AND SELFISHNESS ARE PRODUCTS OF SCARCITY AND CLASS DIVISION.

THERE IS TOO MUCH EVIDENCE THAT PEOPLE WILL FIND WAYS OF WORKING ANY SYSTEM TO SUIT THEIR OWN ENDS.

THE REAL TROUBLE LIES A BIT DEEPER THAN ECONOMICS.

LEAVING MARX ASIDE, NATURALISM IN GENERAL IS FAIRLY DOMINANT IN UNIVERSITIES, SCHOOLS AND "SEATS" OF LEARNING ~ WHY?

55

WE'RE THE ONLY SELF~CONSCIOUS, SELF~DETERMINED BEINGS IN THE UNIVERSE ~ RULERS OF <u>ALL</u>...

··FREE EVEN TO CONTROL THE FUTURE OF OUR OWN EVOLUTION: WHAT MORE COULD A BODY ASK FOR?

IF YOU REALLY WANT TO KNOW~ AND MANY DO NOT, BECAUSE WHERE YOU STOPPED IS A POPULAR PLACE TO STOP— YOU COULD GO BACK TO THE POINT YOU DECIDED TO "FORGET" FOR THE MOMENT.

THERE IS <u>NO</u> BASE FOR ALL THESE ASSUMPTIONS ABOUT HUMAN VALUE; AND BESIDES, THE NOTION OF EXTINCTION AT DEATH IS SO DISTURBING IT UNDERMINES THE POINT OF LIVING.

NIHILISM IS THE NATURAL CHILD OF NATURALISM.

REMEMBER, NATURALISTS HOLD THAT MATTER IS ALL THERE IS, SO WE ARE *MATTER* ONLY.

THEY SAY THE COSMOS IS A CLOSED SYSTEM OF CAUSE AND EFFECT YET THEY TRY TO HOLD ON TO HUMAN FREEDOM.

58

··IT'S STILL NO BASIS FOR HUMAN SIGNIFICANCE.

AND SO LEADS ON TO NIHILISM

ANOTHER ROUTE TO NIHILISM IS: IS IT POSSIBLE TO KNOW?

YOU SEE~ IF WE ARE THE RESULT OF IMPERSONAL FORCES~ EITHER CHANCE OR UNCHANGEABLE LAWS...

THEN WE HAVE NO WAY OF BEING SURE THAT WHAT WE SEEM TO KNOW IS TRUTH OR ILLUSION!

I'M LOST!

·· RUN THAT PAST ME AGAIN, AS THEY SAY.

IF, AS NATURALISTS SAY, PERCEPTION AND KNOWLEDGE ARE BY PRODUCTS OF THE BRAIN, THERE IS NO REASON TO

REMEMBER ~ "THE BRAIN SECRETES THOUGHT AS THE LIVER SECRETES BILE"!

SUPPOSE THAT EVEN HIGHLY ORDERED MATTER HAS ANY INTEREST IN TRUTH OR CORRECT CONCLUSIONS!

HOW CAN WE TEST FOR ILLUSION OR REALITY WITHOUT USING THE BRAIN WE'RE TESTING?

SO NOW..

..WE HAVE A STRANGE SITUATION ~ DARWIN UNABLE TO PROVE HIS OWN THEORY SINCE CONFIDENCE IN LOGIC IS RULED OUT!

"The horrid doubt always arises whether the convictions of man's mind, which has developed from the mind of the lower animals, are of any value or at all trustworthy."

CHARLES DARWIN

WE'RE NOT ONLY BOXED IN BY OUR PAST, ~ OUR ORIGINS IN INANIMATE MATTER..

AMAZING!

"WE'RE BOXED IN BY OUR PRESENT ~ AS THINKERS!

BUT ANY ARGUMENT TO CHECK THE VALIDITY OF AN ARGUMENT IS ITSELF AN ARGUMENT ~ WHICH COULD BE MISTAKEN!

..IT'S LIKE A DOG CHASING ITS TAIL.

BUT VIRTUALLY NO-ONE IS A FULLY PAID-UP NIHILIST.

I'M SIMPLY SHOWING THE IRONY..

That naturalism, born in the Age of Enlightenment, was launched on the belief in the human ability to *know*; yet it leads to nihilism because they have no basis for confidence in their knowing.

61

BUT..

THERE ARE SOME FRIGHTENING IMPLICATIONS IN ALL THIS..

..IF YOU SERIOUSLY BELIEVE YOU CANNOT KNOW, YOU'RE IN DEEP TROUBLE!

YOU SIMPLY COULDN'T FUNCTION!

YET, IT IS THE LOGICAL CONCLUSION.

BUT YOU AND I ARE MORE LIKELY TO MEET THE HALF-BAKED SCEPTIC THAN THE REAL CASES; THERE'S JUST TOO MUCH EVIDENCE THAT KNOWLEDGE IS POSSIBLE..

..WHAT WE NEED IS A WAY TO EXPLAIN WHY WE HAVE IT!

I saw a man pursuing the horizon;
Round and round they sped.
I was disturbed at this;
I accosted the man.
"It is futile," I said,
"You can never —"
"You lie," he cried,
And ran on.

STEPHEN CRANE

The skeptic is never for real. There he stands, cocktail in hand, left arm draped languorously on one end of the mantelpiece, telling you that he can't be sure of anything, not even of his own existence. I'll give you my secret method of demolishing universal skepticism in four words. Whisper to him: "Your fly is open." If he thinks knowledge is so all-fired impossible, why does he always look?

R. F. CAPON

A THIRD ROUTE TO NIHILISM IS...

THE PROBLEM IN THE MORAL AREA IS NOT THAT NATURALISTS ARE NECESSARILY IMMORAL PEOPLE. IT'S MORE THAT THE VALUES MANY OF THEM HOLD HAVE NO BASIS IN THEIR WORLD VIEW.
FOR A NATURALIST, THE WORLD SIMPLY IS THERE.

THE GAP BETWEEN IS AND OUGHT.

ETHICS IS ABOUT WHAT OUGHT TO BE.

"WHETHER IT IS OR NOT.

POLICE

THERE'S NO TRIBE WITHOUT ITS TABOOS~

BUT~ WHICH VALUES ARE TRUE?

MORAL VALUES COULD SIMPLY BE RELEVANT TO THE CULTURE.

BUT WHY IS THE CULTURAL REBEL NOT ALLOWED HIS/HER VIEWS?

BECAUSE THEY UPSET THE STRUCTURE AND THREATEN ITS SURVIVAL.

..SO THE SURVIVAL OF THE CULTURE AS IT IS IS OF MOST IMPORTANCE -WHY? IF WHATEVER IS, IS RIGHT, THEN WHATEVER CHANGE HAPPENS WILL BE RIGHT.

YOU'VE JUST AGREED THAT SOMETHING OUGHT TO BE PRESERVED, IN PREFERENCE TO SOMETHING ELSE ~ YOU'VE MADE A VALUE JUDGMENT!

IF NATURALISM LEADS FROM ALL POINTS TO THIS END··

··WHY AREN'T MORE NATURALISTS NIHILISTS?

IT'S OBVIOUS: THEY DON'T TAKE IT THIS SERIOUSLY.

THEY'RE INCONSISTENT. THEY ACCEPT A SET OF VALUES AND LIVE BY THEM.

NIHILISM IS UNLIVABLE!

YOU CANNOT LIVE A TOTALLY MEANINGLESS LIFE. AS SOON AS YOU TAKE ANY COURSE OF ACTION ~ EVEN FEEDING YOUR- SELF, YOU HAVE GIVEN VALUE TO THAT GOAL. THINGS ARE NOT MEANINGLESS.

THE STRANGEST PARADOX HERE IS THAT MUCH MODERN ART HAS NIHILISTIC IDEOLOGY AT ITS CORE ~ AND YET··

BECKETT, BACON, KAFKA··

··IN THE VERY FACT THAT IT COMMUNICATES MEANINGLESSNESS ~ IT IS NOT MEANINGLESS! - AND THEREFORE NOT TRUE NIHILISM!

YET, SO MUCH SURROUNDS US THAT IS PART NIHILISTIC.

BUT PURE NIHILISM YOU LITERALLY CANNOT LIVE WITH. IT DENIES WHAT EVERY FIBRE OF YOUR BEING CALLS FOR ~ MEANING, VALUE, DIGNITY; DENY THESE CONSTANTLY AND I DOUBT IF YOU CAN SURVIVE.

CHAPTER FIVE

BEYOND NIHILISM

EXISTENTIALISM

".. THE THOUGHT~SHIP "EXISTENTIAL"; THE MISSION ~ TO BOLDLY GO WHERE NO NIHILIST HAS GONE BEFORE!.."

COMING AS IT DOES DIRECTLY FROM NATURALISM, NIHILISM IS THE PROBLEM OF OUR AGE. EXISTENTIALISM..

".. IS AN ANSWER TO IT.

BY THE END OF THE FIRST WORLD WAR, NIHILISM FINALLY BEGAN TO AFFECT THE ATTITUDES OF ORDINARY MEN AND WOMEN.

"A literature of despair is a contradiction in terms ... In the darkest depths of our nihilism I have sought only for the means to transcend nihilism."
ALBERT CAMUS 1950

THE NIGHTMARE OF THE WAR, THE DEPRESSION, THE EVENTUAL RISE OF NAZISM AND ITS HORRORS ALL POINTED TO THE ABSURDITY OF LIFE. MAYBE HUMANS *WERE* MEANINGLESS.

SOUND OF TRUMPETS ~ENTER EXISTENTIALISM TO THE RESCUE!

WHAT ABOUT THE ETHICS PROBLEM?

ETHICS RELATES ONLY TO HUMANS ~BUT THERE'S MORE TO IT THAN BEFORE, BECAUSE THE EXISTENTIALIST'S MAJOR CONCERN IS "HOW CAN I BE SIGNIFICANT IN A MEANINGLESS WORLD?"

TRAVELLING THE SAME ROAD AS NATURALISM WILL ONLY LEAD TO NIHILISM, SO···

··THE EXISTENTIALIST FINDS A FORK IN THE ROAD

··AND TURNS OFF?

NO! ~HE TAKES BOTH!

··AND SPLITS THE WORLD IN TWO!

THE EXTERNAL WORLD OF MATTER, CAUSE AND EFFECT, THE MECHANISMS AND GALAXIES AND GASES, CAN BE KNOWN IN MUCH THE SAME WAY AS I KNOW THIS CUP. THIS THEY CALL THE OBJECTIVE WORLD.

BUT THE OTHER ROAD LEADS OFF TO THE WORLD OF THE MIND, THE PLACE OF AWARENESS AND FREEDOM; WHERE THE INNER AWARENESS OF THE MIND IS A CONSCIOUS PRESENT.

69

NOW COMES THE CORE OF EXISTENTIALISM: IN THE OBJECTIVE WORLD EVERYTHING COMES BEARING ITS OWN NATURE. SALT IS SALT; TREES ARE TREE; ANTS ARE ANT...

"First of all man exists, turns up, appears on the scene, and, only afterwards, defines himself."

J. P. SARTRE

..BUT HUMANS ARE NOT "HUMAN" UNTIL THEY MAKE THEMSELVES TO BE HUMAN~ BY THEIR ACTIONS!

LET'S SAY A SOLDIER FEARS HE'S A COWARD~ IS HE? ONLY IF HE ACTS LIKE ONE.

ONLY WHEN THE BULLETS START TO FLY WILL HIS ACTIONS DECIDE WHAT HE IS.

..SO EACH OF US DEFINES OURSELVES BY OUR ACTIONS.

BECAUSE WE ARE CONSCIOUS, OUR FREE WILL IS IN A DIFFERENT WORLD FROM THE WORLD OF PHYSICS..

..VALUE IS INNER, AND THAT IS MINE TO CONTROL.

BUT ALTHOUGH THESE WORLDS ARE DIFFERENT, THEY MUST MEET. OUR PERCEPTIONS AND IDEAS DO HAVE TO WORK WITH THE FACTS ABOUT THE EXTERNAL WORLD!

~ IF I THINK I CAN STEP OFF A HIGH BUILDING AND FLOAT ~ I'M NOT FACING FACTS ABOUT THE WORLD!

SO THE EXISTENTIALIST WOULD SAY THE OBJECTIVE WORLD IS ABSURD BECAUSE IT HAS ORDER.

WHEREAS THE SUBJECTIVE WORLD, TO HIM THE MORE IMPORTANT, HAS NO IMPOSED ORDER. YET THE TWO "WORLDS" MUST CO-EXIST.

IF WE ARE TO AVOID DESPAIR, WE MUST LEARN TO ACCEPT ABSURDITIES ~ THE GREATEST OF WHICH IS DEATH, FOR WHEN WE DIE, WE BECOME JUST AN OBJECT.

YET WHILE ALIVE AND CONSCIOUS WE CAN CREATE VALUE.

EVER AWARE OF THIS ABSURD COSMOS ~ BUT REBELLING AGAINST IT AND CREATING MEANING.

"The meaning of a man's life consists in proving to himself every minute that he is a man and not a piano key."

DOSTOEVSKY

AND WHERE DO ETHICS COME INTO THIS? HOW CAN THE VALUE OF AN ACTION BE JUDGED?

71

SIMPLE ~ THE GOOD ACTION IS THE CONSCIOUSLY CHOSEN ONE!

SARTRE SAID ~ "BY CHOOSING ~ WE AFFIRM THE VALUE; WE CAN NEVER CHOOSE EVIL, WE WILL ALWAYS CHOOSE THE GOOD." THERE IS NO OUTSIDE STANDARD; GOOD IS WHATEVER A PERSON CHOOSES.

AND EVERY INDIVIDUAL INVENTS HIS, OR HER, OWN ETHIC? RISKY!

BUT AS WE MEET, WE RECOGNIZE THE SUBJECTIVITY OF OTHERS AND THAT OUR ACTIONS AFFECT EACH OTHER. SO, SARTRE CLAIMS, "NOTHING CAN BE GOOD FOR US WITHOUT BEING GOOD FOR ALL!

IF OUR CHOICE IS ALWAYS GOOD ~ IS THERE NO EVIL? OR IS EVIL NOT CHOOSING? I CAN THINK OF A HOST OF ACTIONS IN HISTORY WHERE SOMEONE OBVIOUSLY MADE A WRONG CHOICE!

SINCE GOD DOESN'T FEATURE IN THE ATHEISTIC EXISTENTIALIST'S EQUATION; HOW CAN THERE BE A THEISTIC VERSION?

THE THEISTIC VERSION IS POLES APART FROM THE ATHEISTIC LINE OF THOUGHT.

IN FACT, AT FIRST GLANCE, IT COULD BE TAKEN FOR THEISM!

Theistic Existentialists would accept that God is infinite and personal (Triune), transcendent, immanent, omniscient, sovereign and good. (See pages 13-15.) That he created the cosmos out of nothing to operate by natural laws and yet is open to re-ordering. We are created in God's image, can know something of him and the cosmos, and have a free will. God can and does communicate with us. We were created good but now are fallen and need to be restored by God through Christ. Death for us is either the gate to life with God and his people or life for ever separated from God. Ethics has its base outside of us in the character of God.

I WOULD SAY IT'S NOT JUST THE SAME AT FIRST GLANCE~ IT'S WORD FOR WORD IDENTICAL! WHAT'S DIFFERENT?

The thinking is that where the evidence makes no sense, and reason may lead us to atheism, we can take a leap of faith, and all will be well. Each person is alone in their own subjectivity, and must choose.

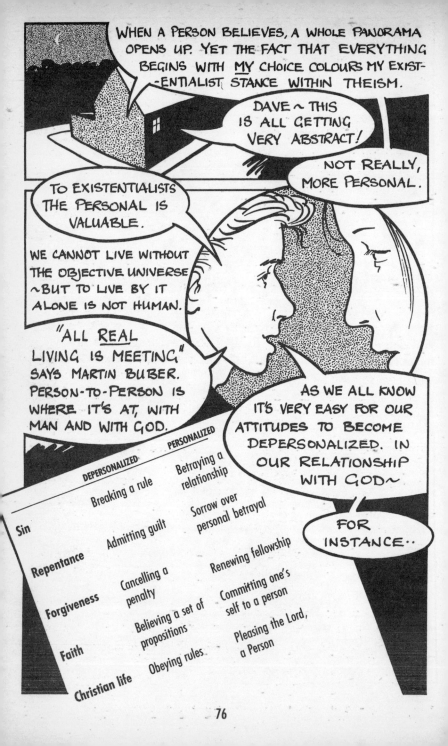

WHEN A PERSON BELIEVES, A WHOLE PANORAMA OPENS UP. YET THE FACT THAT EVERYTHING BEGINS WITH <u>MY</u> CHOICE COLOURS MY EXIST--ENTIALIST STANCE WITHIN THEISM.

DAVE ~ THIS IS ALL GETTING VERY ABSTRACT!

NOT REALLY, MORE PERSONAL.

TO EXISTENTIALISTS THE PERSONAL IS VALUABLE.

WE CANNOT LIVE WITHOUT THE OBJECTIVE UNIVERSE ~BUT TO LIVE BY IT ALONE IS NOT HUMAN.

"ALL <u>REAL</u> LIVING IS MEETING" SAYS MARTIN BUBER. PERSON-TO-PERSON IS WHERE IT'S AT, WITH MAN AND WITH GOD.

AS WE ALL KNOW IT'S VERY EASY FOR OUR ATTITUDES TO BECOME DEPERSONALIZED. IN OUR RELATIONSHIP WITH GOD~

FOR INSTANCE..

	DEPERSONALIZED	PERSONALIZED
Sin	Breaking a rule	Betraying a relationship
Repentance	Admitting guilt	Sorrow over personal betrayal
Forgiveness	Cancelling a penalty	Renewing fellowship
Faith	Believing a set of propositions	Committing one's self to a person
Christian life	Obeying rules	Pleasing the Lord, a Person

THEISTIC EXISTENTIALISTS WOULD ARGUE FOR COLUMN TWO, WHILE THEISTS WOULD SAY BOTH ARE NEEDED.

IN REALITY THE THEIST WORLD VIEW HAS OFTEN BEEN INADEQUATELY UNDERSTOOD...

...AND SOME CHRISTIANS STICK WITH COLUMN ONE.

EMPHASIS ON THE PERSONAL CONTINUES INTO HOW KNOWLEDGE IS RELATED TO THE KNOWER.

IN KIERKEGAARD'S WORK THIS PERSONAL INVOLVEMENT WITH KNOWLEDGE IS VERY STRONG ~ "TO FIND THE TRUTH FOR ME." ~ TRUTH IN THE PERSONAL DIMENSION IS...

"What I really need is to become clear in my own mind *what I must do,* not what I must know — except in so far as knowing must precede every action. The important thing is to understand what I am destined for, to perceive what the deity wants *me* to do."

SOREN KIERKEGAARD

~TRUTH DIGESTED AND LIVED OUT IN LIFE!

RIGHT!

FOR EXAMPLE?

THE FULL TRUTH IS OFTEN PARADOXICAL AND CANNOT BE RESOLVED IN OUR MINDS ALONE ~ IT MUST BE LIVED OUT!

"GOD IS SOVEREIGN ~ YET I MUST ACT." BECOMES "GOD I RELY ON YOU COMPLETELY, DO YOUR WILL. I AM STEPPING OUT TO ACT."

THE PARADOX CAN ONLY BE RESOLVED BY THOUGHT AND ACTION.

AND WAS THAT NOT THE END OF THEIR FAITH?

IT COULD HAVE BEEN.

BUT INSTEAD IT LED TO A RADICAL SHIFT IN EMPHASIS.

THE BIBLE AS *FACT* WAS NOT NOW IMPORTANT BUT IT WAS..

..AS A MODEL OF THE TIME-LESS TRUTHS OF MORALITY.

THE GREAT MYSTERY OF GOD'S ENTRANCE INTO TIME AND SPACE BECAME A MYTH~ A POWERFUL MYTH~ BUT NOT A FACT.

THE FALL DID NOT HAPPEN AT THE DAWN OF MAN..

..IT HAPPENS NOW IN EACH OF US!

THE DEATH AND RESURRECTION OF CHRIST MAY, OR MAY NOT, HAVE OCCURRED..

"An historical fact that involves a resurrection from the dead is utterly inconceivable."

RUDOLF BULTMAN

..WHAT MATTERS IS THE TRANSFORMING EFFECT THE *BELIEF* IN THE RESURRECTION HAD ON THE DISCIPLES!

84

86

ALTHOUGH ALMOST ALL REQUIRE··

SOLITUDE.

AND THERE'S NO INTELLECTUAL CONTENT?

NONE!

THE MOST COMMON PATH INVOLVES CHANTING THE WORD _OM_, OR A PHRASE WITH THAT WORD IN IT

AND "OM" MEANS?

SOME HAVE SUGGESTED MEANINGS — LIKE "YES", "PERFECTION" OR "ALL" ~ BUT IT REALLY DOESN'T MEAN ANYTHING.

THIS IS THE CRUX OF THE DIFFERENCE BETWEEN EASTERN AND WESTERN THOUGHT···

BUT PAUL··

··WE'RE NOT TALKING OF _UNDERSTANDING_, BUT _BECOMING_ ~ ONE WITH THE ONE; BRAHMAN.

··IF BRAHMAN IS IMPERSONAL AND OUR ESSENCE, ATMAN, IS AT ONE WITH BRAHMAN, THAT MEANS THAT, IN OUR TRUEST BEING, WE ARE IMPERSONAL!

87

89

"The world . . . is perfect at every moment : every sin already carries grace within it : all small children are potentially old men, all sucklings have death within them, all dying people — eternal life . . . everything that exists is good — death as well as life, sin as well as holiness, wisdom as well as folly."

HERMAN HESSE
Siddharta

THEISTS WOULD CLAIM THAT, SINCE HUMANS ARE MORAL BEINGS, THEY CAN'T HELP ACTING AS SUCH.

OR, CYNICALLY, WE COULD SAY THAT THEY DO IT FOR SELFISH REASONS..

..AFTER ALL~ WHO WANTS TO COME BACK AS A WORM?

YET, IN SPITE OF THE CONCEPT OF THE INDIVIDUAL IN KARMA, THE PERSON DOES NOT SURVIVE DEATH! ATMAN SURVIVES, BUT ATMAN IS *IMPERSONAL*. WHEN RE-INCARNATED, ATMAN BECOMES *ANOTHER PERSON!*

WELL~ IN THIS VIEW INDIVIDUALITY IS AN ILLUSION ANYWAY. THE REAL ESSENCE WILL SURVIVE; SO DEATH SHOULD BE NO BIG DEAL.

Picture a river when you look at it from a point on the bank. It flows past It was there,
— Now here,
— Then it's past.
Time exists.

THE INDIVIDUAL IS AN ILLUSION...

AND SO TOO IS TIME!

But when you look at the whole river from spring to stream to river to ocean to vapour to rain to spring again, it is a cycle. Time does not exist as past and present : it is a cycle.

..HISTORY IS WHAT APPEARS TO HAPPEN FROM POINTS ON THE BANK ~ AN ILLUSION!

THIS EXPLAINS WHY THE HISTORICAL *FACTS* OF CHRISTIANITY PRESENTED BY WESTERNERS ARE MOSTLY IGNORED IN THE EAST.

IT'S NOT *NOW* OR THE *PAST* THAT MATTERS!

..THAT'S WHY EASTERN SCRIPTURES ARE FILLED WITH PARABLES FABLES, STORIES, MYTHS, POEMS AND SONG...

NO EVENTS IN A SPACE-TIME CONTEXT? UN-REPEATABLE HISTORY?

ALMOST NONE. IT GOES AGAINST THE WHOLE ORDER.

"They all became part of the river. It was the goal of all of them, yearning, desiring, suffering; and the river's voice was full of longing, full of smarting woe, full of insatiable desire. The river flowed on towards its goal ...

... to the waterfall, to the sea, to the current, to the ocean and all goals were reached and each one was succeeded by another. The water changed to vapour and rose, became rain and came down again, became spring, brook and river, changed anew, flowed anew ...

... And all the voices, all the goals, all the yearnings, all the sorrows, all the pleasures, all the good and evil, all of them together were the world ... The great song of a thousand voices consisted of one word: Om — perfection."

HERMAN HESS, Siddharta

IF ACTION IS ILLUSION, ONLY NON-ACTION IS *REALLY* VALUABLE BECAUSE IT IS AN IDEA - NOT AN EVENT.

THE AIM IS TO *CEASE* ACTION AND MEDITATE.

..AND SIMPLY *DIE?*

FINE! ATMAN IS BRAHMAN, BRAHMAN IS ETERNAL: A DEATH TO BE WISHED!

SO, YOU SEE, THERE ARE *HUGE* BARRIERS TO COMMUNICATION BETWEEN EAST AND WEST. FOR THE WESTERNER, SEEING TIME AND REALITY AND REASON AS ILLUSION IS CONFUSING...

...FOR THE EASTERNER, WELL...

...THE *APPARENT* OUTCOME OF KNOWLEDGE, MORALITY AND REASON IN THE WEST IS <u>SO</u> UGLY: *WAR, VIOLENCE*...

...*GREED AND GLUTTONY!*

THOSE WHO WOULD COMMUNICATE THE BEAUTY OF TRUTH IN CHRIST HAVE A TOUGH JOB!

BUT THOSE WHO LOOK EAST FOR MEANING AND SIGNIFICANCE AS INDIVIDUALS HAVE A TOUGHER JOB

...FOR THE PERSON HAS LITTLE VALUE IN THE EAST.

IT IS *NOT* A MORE PEACEFUL, SIMPLER VERSION OF WESTERN LIFE; AN EASTERN STICKING-PLASTER FOR A WESTERN SCRATCH ~ IT'S A *WHOLE NEW WORLD VIEW!*

...*AND LIFESTYLE!*

CHAPTER SEVEN

A SEPARATE REALITY

THE NEW AGE

WITH THE BANK-RUPTCY OF NATURALISM IN THE WEST AND THE HIGH COST TO THE INTELLECT AND THE INDIVIDUAL IN THE EAST..

..PEOPLE ARE GRASPING FOR A HANDLE ON REALITY ~FOR HOPE !

THE NEW AGE WORLD VIEW IS A MINDSET WHOSE TIME HAS COME ~ IT IS NOTHING IF NOT HOPEFUL !

A NEW SPECIES IS EVOLVING !

FOR A WORLD VIEW IN ITS INFANCY, ITS PROPONENTS HAVE ENORMOUS INFLUENCE.

LIKE NATURALISM THERE IS NO TRANSCENDENT GOD IN THIS UNIVERSE. THE EVOLUTIONARY IDEA COMES FROM THE SAME SOURCE.

LIKE BOTH THEISM AND NATURALISM, BUT UNLIKE MONISM, THE INDIVIDUAL IS VERY IMPORTANT...

..IN FACT, MORE THAN EVER!

LIKE MONISM, NEW AGE THOUGHT CENTRES ON MYSTICAL EXPERIENCE. TIME, SPACE AND MORALITY ARE TRANSCENDED, AND REASON IS REJECTED AS A GUIDE TO REALITY.

LIKE ANIMISM THE UNIVERSE IS INHABITED BY SPIRITUAL BEINGS WHO POSSESS VARIOUS TEMPERAMENTS, FROM VICIOUS TO BENEVOLENT, AND MUST BE HUMOURED BY VARIOUS METHODS.
LIFE IS ONE, BUT THE COSMOS CONSISTS OF SPIRIT AND MATTER.
SOME IDEAS COME DRESSED IN DIFFERENT CLOTHES, BUT THEIR ROOTS ARE THE SAME.
"It's almost as if the (human) species were taking a quantum leap into a whole new way of being . . . of such depth and richness . . . that our great, great, grand children may look back upon us as Neanderthals, so different will they be."
JEAN HOUSTON
Foundation for Mind Research N.Y.
MAKE NO MISTAKE A WORLD VIEW OF IMMENSE CULTURAL IMPACT AND PENE-TRATION IS BEING FORMULATED!

96

I CAN SAY I CREATED THE UNIVERSE ~ BUT I DOUBT IF MANY WOULD BELIEVE ME!

BUT IF THAT'S *YOUR* EXPERIENCE, WHO CAN DENY IT?

.. SO LONG AS SEEING IS BEING, SELF-DECEPTION IS A DANGER.

A DANGER? ~ IT'S A CERT!

IMAGINATION IS NOT REALITY ~ WHETHER I LIKE IT OR NOT, CERTAIN LAWS DO GOVERN REALITY.

But only in the *visible* universe. The *invisible* universe is totally different. At the centre of

everything is self, surrounded by the visible universe with which we're directly in touch — the five senses, the laws of nature and all that. *But* — beyond that is the *in*visible universe which the self enters by the doors of perception.

DRUGS AND MEDITATION

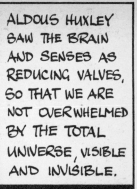

ALDOUS HUXLEY SAW THE BRAIN AND SENSES AS REDUCING VALVES, SO THAT WE ARE NOT OVERWHELMED BY THE TOTAL UNIVERSE, VISIBLE AND INVISIBLE.

··AND BIOFEEDBACK, ACUPUNCTURE, CERTAIN DANCE AND MUSIC AND RITUALS.

THEY FILTER OUT WHAT IS NOT AT THE MOMENT USEFUL, SO EACH OF US IS POTENTIALLY WHAT HE CALLED·· "MIND AT LARGE."

INTERESTING IDEA ~ SOME PEOPLE'S REDUCING VALUES WORK OVERTIME!

KEEP THEM WIDE OPEN! ~ YOU'LL NEED TO, HUXLEY RECKONED ONLY A MEASLY TRICKLE GETS THROUGH!

THESE GUYS ALL HAVE THEIR OWN JARGON~ MIND AT LARGE; EXPANDED CONSCIOUSNESS; A SEPARATE REALITY; SUPERMIND; OTHER SPACES: A SPACE, A PLACE, A CONSCIOUSNESS BEYOND THE VISIBLE UNIVERSE AND ITS LAWS!

TIME AND SPACE ARE ELASTIC.

THE SELF CAN TRAVEL GREAT DISTANCES IN TIME AND SPACE INSTANTLY!

ARE THERE ANY RULES AT ALL?

IN A WAY, ONLY THOSE YOU CREATE...

..AND AS YOU PROGRESS YOU MOVE BEYOND EVEN THOSE!

WHAT IS IT LIKE TO EXPERIENCE "MIND-AT-LARGE"? IS IT THE SAME FOR EVERYONE?

REPORTS OF THINGS LIKE COLOUR ARE SIMILAR ~ ALWAYS INTENSE, LUMINOUS, FAR BEYOND ANY-THING SEEN IN THE "NORMAL" STATE..

..SOME CLAIM THE CAPABILITY OF FLIGHT!

"In the province of the mind, what is believed to be true, 'is' true, or becomes true, — within limits to be found experientially and experimentally. These limits are further beliefs to be transcended. In the province of the mind — there are *no* limits."

JOHN LILLY
The Centre of the Cyclone

THE INTENSITY PROBABLY REINFORCES THE FEELING THAT WHAT IS SEEN IS MORE REAL THAN ANYTHING SEEN IN THE VISIBLE WORLD!

BUT YOU CAN'T JUST IGNORE THE VISIBLE UNIVERSE. LOOK AT US—HERE, NOW..

WE'RE IN THIS ROOM, NOT SOMEWHERE ELSE; THIS IS TODAY, NOT YESTERDAY OR TOMORROW!

TO HAVE HEAT TO KEEP WARM IS GOOD ~ TO SET FIRE TO THE FLAT IS NOT!

THESE ARE PERCEPTIONS TOO. THEY'RE REAL!

YES, BUT FOR THOSE IN THE NEW AGE, THEY'RE THE REALITIES OF...

..THE STRAIGHT THINKING ORDINARY CONSCIOUSNESS.

THEY ARE BUT A SHADOW OF THE REAL THING! WHAT IS EXPERIENCED THROUGH COSMIC CONSCIOUSNESS SEEMS SO MUCH MORE REAL THAN THE REALITY OF THE VISIBLE WORLD.

"Along with the consciousness of the cosmos there occurs an intellectual enlightenment which alone would place the individual on a new plane of existence — would make him a member of a new species ... With these come what may be called a sense of immortality, a consciousness of eternal life, not a conviction that he shall have this but the consciousness that he has it already."

R. M. BUCKE

BUT IF WHAT YOU SEE IS REAL, THEN THESE "HELLS" ARE REAL!

..AND ANYWAY, IF THE SELF IS GOD, SURELY IT CAN CREATE AT WILL?

IF HELL APPEARS, DESTROY IT AND CREATE A HEAVEN; WHY NOT?

SELF, IT SEEMS, DOES NOT ALWAYS REALIZE THAT IT IS GOD. SHIRLEY MacLAINE EXPLAINS THAT:

"Individual souls became separated from the higher vibration in the process of creating various life forms. Seduced by the beauty of their own creations they became entrapped in the physical, losing their connection with Divine Light. The panic was so severe that it created a battlefield known to you now as good and evil."

..AND WE MUST REVERSE THIS FALL. THAT'S THE EVOLUTIONARY GOAL.

BUT IF THE SELF REALLY IS GOD, IT COULD NOT NOT KNOW IT! IT'S A CONTRADICTION!

CONTRADICTIONS DON'T SEEM TO STOP PEOPLE BELIEVING!

105

AND HOW IS DEATH VIEWED?

WELL, OBVIOUSLY, STATES OF CONSCIOUSNESS WOULD CONFIRM US TO BE MUCH MORE THAN OUR PHYSICAL BODIES, ~SAY NEW AGERS.

THERE'S A HEAVY INTEREST IN NEAR-DEATH AND OUT-OF-THE-BODY EXPERIENCES AND PAST-LIFE RECALL.

STANISLAV GROF GIVES L.S.D. TO PATIENTS BEFORE THEY DIE, SO THAT THEY MAY EXPERIENCE COSMIC CONSCIOUSNESS AS THEY PASS BEYOND THE VISIBLE WORLD.

SO NEW AGERS BELIEVE IN REINCARNATION?

YES ~ I THOUGHT I'D MENTIONED THAT EARLIER··

··MAYBE NOT. SHIRLEY MacLAINE··

AGAIN!

YEAH ~ SHE'S DEFINITELY THEIR FRONT PERSON, SO FAR AS THE PUBLIC ARE CONCERNED!

108

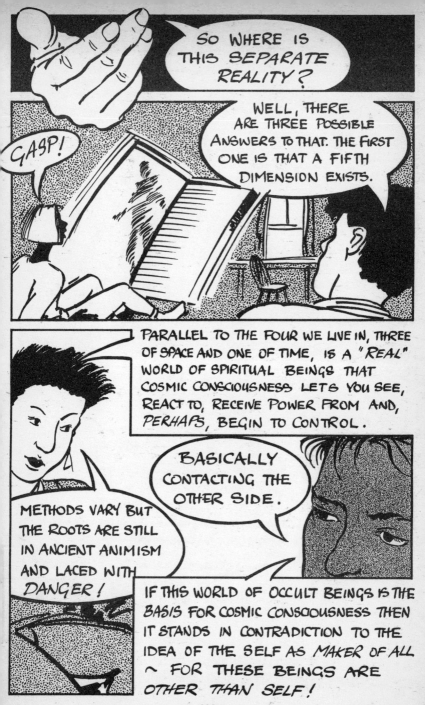

109

·· OR DOES THE SELF EVEN CONTROL THESE BEINGS IN THE SEPARATE UNIVERSE?

"There is a posthumous state ... a blissful visionary experience ... also a hell of appalling visionary experience; and ... beyond time ... union with the divine ground."

ALDOUS HUXLEY

THOSE WHO WOULD CONTROL, MAY THEM-SELVES BE CONTROLLED!

~ LOCKED IN THE JAWS OF A DEMONIC TRAP!

YOU THINK THAT SOUNDS DRAMATIC, PAUL? OCCULT BONDAGE IS UNFORTUN-ATELY NOT UNCOMMON.

THE SECOND ANSWER IS THE PSYCHEDELIC VERSION.

SOUNDS "COSMICALLY" LATE SIXTIES!

IT JUST MEANS THAT THE WORLD EXPERIENCED ORIGINATES IN THE PSYCHE OF THE PERSON EXPERIENCING IT. THE PERSON DOES NOT SO MUCH OPEN "DOORS OF PERCEPTION" AS CREATE A NEW REALITY TO PERCEIVE!

STILL LEAVES THE BAD TRIP PROBLEM. IF YOU'RE THE CREATOR WHY NOT CREATE A GOOD ONE?

·· NOR DOES IT ANSWER THE QUESTION, "IS IT REAL?"~ IF IT'S TOTALLY SELF-GENERATED.

NOW THE THIRD VERSION: HAVE YOU EVER HEARD OF BENJAMIN WHORF? HE HAS AN INTERESTING IDEA ~

"The structure of the language one habitually uses influences the manner in which one understands his environment. The picture of the universe shifts from tongue to tongue."

BENJAMIN WHORF

MM, ONE TO THINK ABOUT!

AND YET..

·· THE IMPLICATION HAS BEEN POINTED OUT AS ~ "THE COMPLETE DISSOLUTION OF ANY ALLEGED TRUTH CONTENT OF LANGUAGE" [1]

YOU ONLY NEED —

THE IDEA IS THAT "ALL PERCEPTION IS A KIND OF SYMBOLIC SYSTEM ·· THERE IS NO DIRECT AWARENESS OF REALITY AT ALL." [2] SO, IF YOU WANT A NEW WORLD..

A NEW SET OF SYMBOLS!

1 Ernst Cassirer.   2 Robert Masters

111

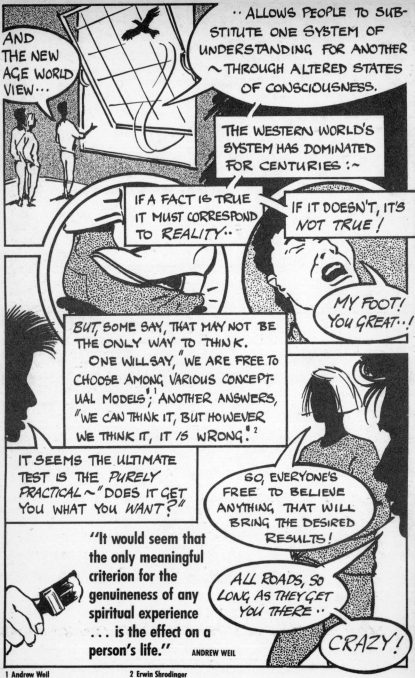

"Had I created everything or had it created me? How could either be proved? But if my reality was a question of what I perceived it to be then ... *I made* the *choice*. I was the one empowered with the decision making process of how to relate to it. So in point of truth, what difference did it make? I was the one *choosing how* to experience life."

SHIRLEY MacLAINE

THAT SEEMS TO BE THE VERY ESSENCE OF NEW AGE THOUGHT; THAT EACH OF US IS THE *CENTRE* OF OUR OWN *REALITY*, AND SO THE CENTRE OF *ALL REALITY*!

EVEN IF NOT ITS CREATOR WE STILL DECIDE WHAT IS *REAL* *FOR US*!

AND, MacLAINE ASKS, "WAS THAT WHY I WAS ALL THERE WAS?··· WAS THIS WHAT WAS MEANT BY THE STATEMENT, 'I AM THAT I AM'?"

I SEE AN AWESOME DIFFERENCE BETWEEN OURSELVES AND THE GOD WHO MADE THAT STATEMENT. TO ME THE *ULTIMATE* CHOICE IS ···

EACH PERSON IS EITHER GOD·· OR *NOT GOD*··

IF GOD, THEN *EVERYTHING* IS POSSIBLE AND PERMITTED; BUT·· IF *NOT GOD*···

..THEN EVERYTHING MUST BOW TO THE JUDGMENT OF GOD.

BUT, ANYWAY, HOW CAN EVERYONE BE GOD? HOW DO OTHERS FEATURE IN MacLAINE'S UNDERSTANDING OF REALITY?

IT SEEMS THAT EVEN THOUGH SHE SELLS MILLIONS OF HER BOOKS, SHE'S NOT SURE IF THOSE WHO BUY THEM *ARE REAL!*

THAT'S A PUZZLE...

"I could legitimately say that I created the Statue of Liberty, chocolate chip cookies, the Beatles, terrorism, and the

Vietnam War. I couldn't really say for sure whether anyone else in the world had actually experienced those things separately from me because these people existed as individuals only in my dream. I knew *I* had created the reality of the evening news at night. It was in my reality. But whether anyone else was experiencing the news *separately* from me was unclear, because *they* existed in my reality too. And if they reacted to world events, then I was creating them to react so I would have someone to interact with, thereby enabling myself to know me better."

SHIRLEY MacLAINE
It's All in the Playing

EVERYBODY'S OUT THERE JUST SO THAT I CAN "KNOW ME BETTER"!

..IT'S SO INCREDIBLY SELF-CENTRED ~ AND SO INCREDIBLY INCONSISTENT!

115

116

117

THE ROMAN CHURCH STILL CARRIES ON THIS IDEA IN MARY AND THE SAINTS...

..BUT SUCH A "HIGH" VIEW OF GOD IS REALLY A LOW VIEW OF HIS CHARACTER, AND TENDS TO OVER EXALT THE SAINTS.

A SAINT IS SIMPLY A MEMBER OF CHRIST'S CHURCH, AND ANGELS ARE AT GOD'S SOLE COMMAND.

GOD MAY BE FAR BEYOND US, BUT HE HAS CONTACTED US!

"Let no-one be found among you who sacrifices his son or daughter in the fire, who practises divination or sorcery, interprets omens, engages in witchcraft, or casts spells, or who is a medium or spiritist, or who consults with the dead. Anyone who does these things is detestable to the Lord."
DEUTERONOMY 18: 10-12

SO, IF GOD HIMSELF IS FOR US, WE NEED LOOK NO FURTHER THAN HIM!

118

119

120

CHAPTER EIGHT

1 BRUCE COCKBURN

THIRD~A WORLD VIEW SHOULD EXPLAIN WHAT IT CLAIMS TO EXPLAIN!

SOME NATURALISTS EXPLAIN MORALITY AS THE METHOD BY WHICH HUMANS SURVIVE, BUT THEY ASSUME THAT HUMANS *SHOULD* SURVIVE!

"BUT *WHY?*.. THEY DON'T SAY.

QUESTIONS AND *MORE* QUESTIONS!

IF YOU WANT ANSWERS, YOU MUST PUT THE QUESTIONS. YOU MUST BE SATISFIED THAT YOUR WORLD VIEW IS *TRUE!*

IF THERE'S EVEN A TINY CRACK, IT MAY GROW TO SPLIT THE PEACE OF YOUR WORLD.

"The crucial questions, then, to ask of a world view are, How does it explain the fact that human beings think but think haltingly, love but hate too, are creative but also destructive, wise but often foolish, and so forth? What explains our longing for truth or personal fulfilment? Why is pleasure, as we know it now, rarely enough to satisfy completely? Why do we usually want more — more money, more love, more ecstasy? How do we explain our human refusal to operate in an amoral fashion?"

JAMES W. SIRE

ULTIMATELY TRUTH IS THE ONLY THING THAT WILL SATISFY US. SO ANY UNEASY FEELING THAT WHAT WE BELIEVE DOESN'T FIT WELL TOGETHER SHOULD BE INVESTIGATED ...

BECAUSE, EVEN IF WE BURY OUR DOUBT, IT WILL RISE TO THE SURFACE.

125

"The world is charged with the grandeur of God.
   It will flame out, like shining from shook foil;
   It gathers to a greatness, like the ooze of oil
Crushed. Why do men then now not reck his rod?
Generations have trod, have trod, have trod;
   And all is seared with trade; bleared, smeared with toil;
   And wears man's smudge and shares man's smell; the soil
Is bare now, nor can foot feel, being shod.

And for all this, nature is never spent;
   There lives the dearest freshness deep down things;
And though the last lights off the black West went
   Oh, morning, at the brown brink eastward, springs —
Because the Holy Ghost over the bent
   World broods with warm breast and with ah! bright wings."

GERARD MANLEY HOPKINS

127